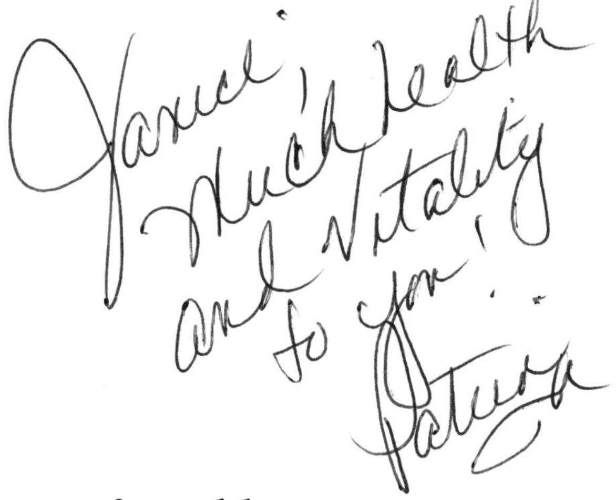

Organically Yours

Open Yourself to a Vibrant Healthy Life Through Clean Living

Patricia Diesel

Keep It Simple Now, LLC

Legal Disclaimer

Organically Yours

Open Yourself to a Vibrant Healthy Life

Through Clean Living

Keep It Simple Now, LLC

14 Cottage Street

Basking Ridge, NJ 07920

ISBN: 978-0-9789303-4-9

Library of Congress Catalog Number: 2017909488

This book is intended to provide general information only. Neither the author nor publisher provide any legal or other professional advice. If you need

You are responsible for doing your research and determining which products are best for you.

Connect with Patricia

Email: Patricia@patriciadiesel.com

Website: www.patriciadiesel.com

Facebook: www.facebook.com/keepitsimplenow

Twitter: www.twitter.com/keepitsimplenow

Instagram: www.instagram.com/patriciadieselcoach

LinkedIn: www.linkedin.com/in/patriciadiesel

Dedication

To My Heavenly Father

There would be no light without you.
I am in awe of you, always.
Thank you, thank you, thank you!

To My Mom

I see clearly the gifts you provided throughout my life. I will always be grateful for your devotion and love. My love is endless… until we meet again.

To My Dad

Your kindness is a quality that I can only hope to measure up to. Thank you for showing me what really matters most in life.
I love you dearly.

To My Daughter

You are my soulful connection to life. You have given me more than a lifetime supply of love. Thank you for always being my best friend. My heart is filled with love for you!

To My Siblings

Life is a cycle that takes us on an interesting ride. Through it all, we do our best to hold on. Thank you for not letting go. I love you all.

To My Friends

Words cannot describe what your moral support means to me. I feel deeply grateful and blessed to be kindred spirits.

To My Medical Support Team

Your insight and guidance is invaluable. I am so glad I found you in time. Thank you for caring and guiding me towards a healthier life.

To My Clients

Thank you for trusting me and inspiring me to be a better coach. It is an awesome gift and honor to be part of your journey.

To My Editor

Words cannot describe my gratitude for your help and contribution to this book. Thank you from the bottom of my heart.

Acknowledgments

As a child, I had an inquisitive nature. Having only one answer to my question did not always satisfy my curiosity. This is why coaching has helped me tremendously in life.

As a student of coaching, I have a deep appreciation for the skill and devotion it takes to help guide and transform people's lives. To have the opportunity to help people by being a coach is an incredible honor — one I do not take lightly.

Coaching has taught me to keep an open mind and to keep seeking the truth. It is in that spirit along with my promise to God that I had the resolve to find alternative methods and practices to change the outcome of my health.

I am grateful to the community of like-minded practitioners that envelop and demonstrate their commitment to care for their patients and clients.

With continued education and missionary spirits, I am hopeful that we will see greater improvement in future generations with our approach to wellness.

Your work is valued and needed…in so many ways.

In wellness,

Patricia Diesel

Testimonials

Patricia has captured the true essence of living a clean life. It has been a great joy to help her heal and I'm delighted she is sharing her recovery to inspire and help others to take back their health as well.

~ Brooke Goldner, M.D.
Author of Goodbye Lupus

This book will help you see that vibrant health is well within reach with a clean, organic lifestyle. Patricia provides powerful examples of how to do this through her own unique journey to well-being.

~ Dr. Henele
Doctor of Naturopathic Medicine
Author of Energetic Health; Interesting Insights Into Advanced Natural Medicine

Patricia's proactive approach to her personal wellness demonstrates her commitment to living a healthy, balanced life.

~ Laine S. Higa, O.D.
Clinical Instructor, Dry Eye Service
The Eye Institute of the Pennsylvania College of Optometry

This book will inspire you. Patricia's system to helping people live an organized, clean life is invaluable. Her insight, experience and practical tools encourage healthy, Clean Living.

~ David F. Tolin, Ph.D. ABPP
Director, Anxiety Disorders Center,
The Institute of Living Adjunct Professor of Psychiatry, Yale University School of Medicine

Patricia's proactive approach and commitment to implementing lifestyle changes played an integral role in her rapid healing. Usually we see patients make gradual improvements over a course of time. Within four months we saw a 90% recovery of her condition due to her relentless spirit and dedication to Clean Living.

~ John Barbato, O.D.
Eyecare, MD of New Jersey

Table of Contents

Chapter 1:
The Wake-Up Call

Once you wake up and smell the coffee, it's hard to go back to sleep.

Fran Drescher

Have you ever been totally caught off guard by something that would change your life forever? It happened to me…

It was a February morning just like every other winter morning on the East Coast. Extreme cold, lots of snow, sleet and shrunken daylight. It was the kind of day where you want to stay under the covers, but you get up because you must. You find yourself longing for the day when you can move to a warmer climate and resign yourself to being a snow bird.

That morning, I was getting excited about the mini get-away I had planned. The prospect of being in the sunshine and grabbing a little vitamin D and a sun-kissed tan was tantalizing. Little did I know, my body was getting ready to surprise me in a way that would redirect my life forever.

Bare feet on a cold ceramic floor was enough of a shock, but when I looked into the mirror, I couldn't believe what I saw. The image that peered back at me was barely recognizable. My face was inflamed and discolored.

Overnight, a rash had erupted across the bridge of my face. There was severe swelling around my forehead and eye area with slight bruising underneath. My eyes were very sensitive to light and I felt a consistent, yet at times, sharp, burning pain.

Of course, I did what anyone would do. I sought medical help. There was speculation of what my doctor 'thought' was wrong with me. He handed me a prescription and told me to see an eye doctor as soon as possible.

I was so grateful my optometrist was able to see me immediately. I was given a diagnosis of Chronic Dry Eye and Meibomian Gland Dysfunction. However, he could not pinpoint what had prompted the rash, bruising, and severe swelling.

After numerous visits, my eyes remained unstable and I was experiencing cornea complications. With no end to my chronic pain in sight, I quickly realized that I needed to take matters into my own hands. This provoked me to go back to my original doctor and request further testing.

As you can imagine, waiting for the results was like sitting on pins and needles. After relentless follow-up calls, the doctor's office eventually confirmed they had my paperwork. Since the doctor was not available to speak with me, I immediately went to their office to pick up my lab results.

I was disconcerted to learn that once again, he had no intention of scheduling any follow-up appointments to discuss my course of action. Instead, he wrote on the lab report that I should follow-up with a rheumatologist since my results showed a positive ANA (antinuclear antibodies) and RNP (ribonucleoprotein) associated with Systemic Lupus Erythematosus (SLE).

Lupus? What does that mean? How sick am I? Am I going to die? There was no human interaction; all I had were words on paper.

I felt dehumanized as I was still absorbing the shock of what I was reading.

I began calling rheumatologists in hopes of finding one that could see me as quickly as possible. The booking time for a new patient ranged from four to twelve weeks wait.

How can I wait for one to three months before I see a doctor to begin my healing process? I asked myself. I decided to call every day to see if there were any cancellations and every day I grew more frustrated and exhausted.

I had been thrown into a medical crisis and no one was there to help me, offer support or even educate me on what was happening. *At least guide me on what I can do in the meantime to help myself,* I thought. Eventually I received the call that an opening was available.

The appointment with the rheumatologist was another discouraging experience. She asked, "Why are you here? We usually see patients who are in worse conditions than you! Many people have false positives with this type of test. Just because you have a positive result doesn't mean you have it."

When I asked her what would happen

if I did test positive, she told me that the probable course of action for me would be to take a chemotherapy pill. However, based on my health history, I knew that I could suffer adverse reactions.

I shared my concern that I was not in favor of taking the medication. She told me that the alternative would be for me to do nothing and wait until the disease attacked my organs, which would eventually lead to kidney failure.

Although the rheumatologist did mention that exercise and having a good diet to combat stress would be helpful, there was no further discussion about how to heal from the inside out or what a healthy lifestyle plan might look like.

The information she gave me was distressing but it was her lack of compassion and cold bedside manner that devastated me the most.

I left the appointment feeling as though I had wasted her time. Despair, confusion, isolation, frustration, anger and overwhelm tried to set in. But I made the choice not to go there.

Instead, I began to think back to the questionnaire the rheumatologist had me fill out. I realized that I had been experiencing various symptoms for a long time. Symptoms such as burning on the soles of my feet, swelling in my ankles, joint pain, muscle ache, stiff neck, stomach issues, interrupted sleep patterns and pain in my teeth and eyes.

I had been seeing doctors, dentists and eye specialists about all these issues individually, yet they could never identify the root cause. I was left searching for answers.

I convinced myself that these individual difficulties were something I would have to live with — 'the price of aging.' I never considered that something was seriously wrong with me.

It was in that time period that I decided that I needed to become my own 'health detective' and advocate. I wasn't content to wait for the health care system any longer. I fervently searched the library and internet. I was on a quest for knowledge and couldn't be stopped.

My well-being was compromised and I only had myself to rely on. I was on a mission to figure it out. The alternative was not an option. Here's what I learned…

Food is medicine, not just fuel. Our cellular bodies are designed to heal themselves. Plant-based foods provide rich nutrients to repair and heal our bodies. By choosing foods that were toxic, I had created an environment that broke my body down, not build it up.

During this time of discovery, I found a wealth of information and a doctor, Brooke Goldner, M.D. (author of Goodbye Lupus), who has been successful in reversing auto-immune disease with an anti-inflammatory, plant-based diet, including healing herself from Lupus, just using her nutrition protocol.

I started to detox with organic smoothies and followed her protocol and found myself healing from the pain. The focus moved from whether or not I had an autoimmune disease to focusing on healing my symptoms.

Was the transition difficult at first? Absolutely. I cried, I was scared, I prayed, I was still dealing with a lot of uncertainty… *was I going to be okay?* I reminisced of the days that I could eat whatever I wanted and fought to not give into the temptation. I knew that resisting certain foods (no matter how much I longed for them) would only benefit me in the long run.

After I started to make the change, several amazing things started to happen. My eyes weren't as swollen, the pain diminished and my sleep improved. Was I really healing by simply eliminating dairy, eggs, meat, fish, pasta and bread from my eating habits? How could drinking a gallon of water a day help this much? There was only one way to find out.

I found another rheumatologist and made an appointment (well in advance this time) to get blood work done. When I finally had my appointment, I was tested for everything that could possibly be wrong with my immune system.

It took two weeks for the results, but I tested negative for everything. To my surprise, she nodded her head and said, "Whatever you're doing, keep doing it." This was confirmation that regardless of whether the initial diagnosis was accurate, initiating these healthy practices gradually eliminated my SLE symptoms.

And the issue with my Chronic Dry Eye and Meibomian Gland Dysfunction? These conditions usually take a year or longer to see significant signs of improvement. To my surprise, as I was working on healing my body, my eyes started to heal as well.

In four months time, I made a rapid restoration to 90% wellness, and it feels wonderful! I would like to add that adhering daily to a vital eye care regiment was a necessary component as well.

However, I am convinced that the change of diet played an integral role in my speedy recovery.

So why am I sharing my story with you? Because I don't want anyone to go through the pain and frustration I experienced. I don't want you to wait for a serious medical crisis to hit you before you take action.

We have been conditioned to not do anything about our health until there is a problem. I am hoping that through this book you will see that the best course of action is preventative care to avoid getting sick in the first place.

Who is this book for? This book is perfect for three categories of people. The only two qualifications anyone needs are a willingness to learn and the ability to act on what you have read. Since you are reading this book, you qualify!

First, I want to reach fit, health-conscious people who want to stay that way. People who recognize that maintaining their well-being is important and intentional. People who realize that they need to bring balance to all areas of their life to keep their good health.

The second category I want to reach are those people who are starting to "feel off." Are you noticing little symptoms that the doctors can't figure out? You will want to take a proactive approach to getting better — before things get worse!

Finally, I want to reach those who are already sick — people who have been diagnosed with autoimmune diseases. They know they need to make radical changes to their lifestyle. They don't want to cover the symptoms with medication; they want to heal their bodies.

I'm just a regular person who was caught off guard by a potentially serious diagnosis. I was not going to take the traditional method that most physicians suggest to just mask my symptoms. I chose to address my symptoms differently.

We have been programmed to want a quick fix, which only costs us more in the long run. Not only because of the rising medication expense, but the harmful side effects and drug interactions it can cause people.

What is the solution? Open yourself up to a vibrant, healthy life through Clean Living. Detoxify your body, break negative thought patterns and have a smart, uncluttered environment that promotes balance and peace in your life. Experience the dynamic benefits of radical change.

So, come join me on the journey to being your own health advocate and taking a proactive approach to your wellness. You don't have to wait until a true health crisis occurs. You can begin healing yourself through Clean Living today. Let's begin…

Chapter 2:
A Fresh, Fit, Forward Life

***No matter what the situation,
you have a choice.***

Deepak Chopra

How strong is your desire for a fresh, fit, forward life? On a scale of 1 to 10, where would you fall? Are you just curious about Clean Living and want to make some changes in your life, or are you in a situation where you are suffering with poor or deteriorating health?

What if you choose a 4 or 5 out of 10? Does that mean you shouldn't read this book? Of course not. If you are curious, you will find this book a great start. It will give you the knowledge you need to decide how to move towards Clean Living and increase your desire to carry it through.

The person who will benefit the most from this book is someone who desires to change their life. The practical wisdom shared in this handbook will help you transform your life by making personal decisions that will assist in healing your body through lifestyle choices.

ஓ৶

The Clean Living Concept

Clean Living is a movement with a deep-rooted history. The Clean Living concept that I am introducing for the purpose of this book stresses more than just nutritional health.

This method puts greater emphasis on our overall health by taking a comprehensive approach to our body, mind and environment. Clean Living represents a:

✓ Fit & Nourished Body
✓ Forward-Thinking Mind
✓ Fresh, Free Environment

By taking this all-inclusive approach, a synergy among the body, mind and environment occurs. Each area is equal to its counterpart and relies on the other to sustain harmony and balance for whole living. The concept of having all three parts in unison encourages healthy practices for a vibrant, healthy life.

When I realized what was happening to my body, it made me look at my entire life. For the most part, I was very happy. I was content in my environment. I live in a simple, yet aesthetically pleasing cottage that nourishes my soul. I have the awesome privilege of being a coach to other people, which feeds my mind.

Now that I have implemented the changes I discuss in this book, I can truly say that my life is more in balance. Isn't this the type of life that you want? To be happy, healthy and enjoy life? It is possible. Remember, the concept of Clean Living is to be proactive in the three areas that matter the most: your body, mind and environment. Let's examine each aspect in turn.

Fit & Nourished Body

A fit and nourished lifestyle includes choosing organic foods that sustain and heal your body. The starting point is learning and being mindful of what you ingest, and understanding the importance of nutrition in terms of healing.

Have you ever felt sluggish and sleepy after eating a meal? This can be the effect of foods that don't agree with you. Good, nutritious foods will energize you and motivate you to do more.

If we look at our bodies as hosts for our sacred selves, then it only makes sense to provide them with the proper nourishment and care. One of the best ways to ensure that we keep our bodies healthy is by keeping them in an alkaline state. Having an alkaline body makes it difficult for inflammation to survive. Think of it as creating a barrier against disease and toxins that can harm us.

Here is what I experienced when I started to heal my body:

✓ More energy

✓ Better sleep

✓ Hydrated skin

✓ Whiter teeth

✓ Strong nails

✓ Clear eyes

✓ Joints that don't hurt

✓ Muscles that don't ache

✓ Weight loss
✓ No more bloating

Forward-Thinking Mind

Modern stress is real, and most of us feel the overwhelming effects it can have on our mind. Stress can affect the way we think and affect our attitude towards life. Our minds are amazing machines that can empower us to accomplish wonderful things or prevent us from achieving our best.

Did you know that our minds are designed to create chemical grooves that reinforce positive or negative thoughts? Everything you think either fortifies an existing groove or creates a new one. These paths create patterns that influence your decision-making process, your behavior and your results.

So, over time, repeated positivity creates a peaceful, rewarding life, and negativity produces unhappiness, bitterness, stress and regret.

Have you been living with negative thoughts like bitterness, guilt and regret? The good news is that we possess the ability to change the grooves over time. We can create a forward-thinking positive attitude and adjust the way we view our lives.

We begin by being mindful of what we are focusing on: constructive (positive) or destructive (negative) thoughts. If we are too focused on the past or too much into the future, it can keep us from living in the present.

Thinking too much into the future leads to worry, anxiety and fear. Feeling anxious about what's to come, too much to do, or whether we will have it perfect or not, has a twofold effect: it depletes our energy and ramps up our nervous system. In both cases, we become out of balance and put greater stress on our health.

The present is the best place to be. The "Now" is a GIFT for us to enjoy: it is the place where it all happens. Feeding our mind good, happy, creative, loving, nurturing thoughts and focusing on the now brings us an exceptional, satisfying life.

So how do we open our minds to pure, positive thoughts to create a better life?

First, it begins with awareness. Awareness of our negative thought patterns that keep us hostage to worry and anxiety. Second, we consciously choose to replace negative thoughts with positive reinforcement and third, we use meditation and prayer to keep our mind at peace.

Here is what I experienced:

✓ Clearer thinking

✓ Improved memory

✓ More motivation

✓ Happier disposition

✓ Calmer stance

Fresh, Free Environment

Just as we discussed the importance of honoring our bodies, it is equally vital to honor our sacred living space. Having a home where we can easily find our things, that is aesthetically pleasing and we feel proud to live in, does wonders for our well-being.

It's not about having a perfect home (there's no such thing). It is however about bringing out the best in ourselves so we live freely and comfortably in our dwelling. Doing our best to create a neat and tidy environment is clean, healthy living at its best. Add green plants, organic natural products and air purifiers and — well, maybe "perfect" isn't that far out of reach.

It has been proven that a messy, disorganized home creates mental stress.This puts additional stress on our body. When our home is functional, it makes it much easier to keep our mind in a positive place. Staying in a healthy mindset helps us carve out the time to nourish our body and get proper rest.

Another aspect of our environment is the people we associate with: our friends and loved ones. It is difficult, if not impossible to have vibrant, inspiring, uplifting thoughts that encourage successful actions when the friends that you spend the most time with are constantly dragging you down.

A few years ago, my friend Kim found herself in a difficult position. She had come to the realization that her life needed to change, so she started to implement small changes in her life.

She was so excited about the results that she was seeing that she started to tell her friends. Imagine her shock when they put down every idea she shared, even though she could prove that they worked!

The negativity grew to the point where Kim had to make a decision. Her friends' negativity had begun to affect the progress that she was seeing in her life because she was always second-guessing herself.

Finally, she realized that it was time to let some of those people go and find new friends that would uplift and encourage her to live a great life.

It was difficult at first, but over time, Kim came to realize that her life was growing by leaps and bounds once she didn't have pessimistic people holding her back.

Our home is our sanctuary. A place where our mind and body get to rest and be free. An environment where people exude love, kindness and support is the hallmark of Clean Living.

Here is what I experienced:

✓ A treasured space that inspires the mind and soul

✓ Comfortable surroundings to rest my body

✓ Clean surroundings that support my health

I love to share stories of people whose lives have been changed by making their body, mind and environment priorities in their lives. Their stories inspire me to take my journey to the next level and I hope that they will do the same for you.

ଛଠ

Harry's Story

I met Harry while he was working on the set of a popular morning TV show. I immediately liked his attitude towards life. He was recently divorced, had two kids and he had just bought his first house. As we talked, he revealed to me that he really didn't know how to make his home into an inviting place. He longed for a home that was "guest-ready" and where his children felt proud to bring their friends over to visit.

And so, our journey began. Here is what Harry had to say about the changes in his life. "Where do I start? Clean Living has made it easy when somebody wants to stop by. I'm not nervous about having visitors anymore because I have nothing to hide. With my house being clean, it's easier for me to rest.

Although you may think you are too tired to keep it clean, you will discover that you get better rest when you live in a clean environment. There is a different kind of energy in the room. A clean environment, whether it's my home, office or car, inspires and energizes me. Which translates into better sleep and waking up refreshed.

When I eat properly, I feel better and I'm more energized. I have more energy for everything, including home projects and my hobbies. I have more energy to devote to my relationships and social life.

When I eat well, exercise well and sleep well, I am running at my optimum best. I can expect peak performance from my body when I take care of myself. Now I am more confident in every aspect of my life. I feel stronger mentally, like I can accomplish more. Clean Living helps me know that I can move forward in life.

By eating clean, and living in a fresh environment — it gives my mind renewed vigor, more stamina. I am more ambitious and positive. I don't want to sit on the couch and veg out and eat bad food."

They Are All Interconnected In A Gradual Process

When all three areas of your life are in harmony, everything else tends to organically fall into place. It's a *gestalt*: the sum of the whole is greater than the sum of the separate parts.

We may see some improvement in our lives by focusing on eating well, exercising, or being mindful. We may enjoy greater peace in taking care of our homes. But, if we work on all three disciplines together, the benefits increase tenfold.

Many people who try to achieve Clean Living become overwhelmed by trying to do too much all at once. If they don't see the results they are looking for right away, they are prone to frustration and defeat.

Be gentle with change. Any type of sustainable adjustment requires your patience and a healthy dose of commitment to change your life. You must ask yourself, "What is my alternative?" The alternative is to go back to those old habits that don't serve us. Even when we know that it can potentially hurt us in the long run.

By keeping up with the process, it will soon become a lifestyle that feels natural to you and will integrate into your routine. In time, you will see that the benefits far outweigh the alternatives.

The Starting Place

One of the questions I get asked most frequently is *where to start. "Should I begin with my body, mind or environment first?"* That is a smart question. Happily, there is no right or wrong answer! Each person has individual needs and what worked for me may not be the best place for you.

So, what should you do? I have two recommendations. First, become your own health detective. Throughout this book, you will discover many helpful resources, including a section at the end of the book that you can use to research your personal needs and determine the essential place to start.

Second, let me be your guide on this journey. While I am not a medical professional, my experiences as a certified professional coach, author, public speaker and professional organizer have made me uniquely qualified to encourage you on your journey.

I am offering a free 30-minute personal consultation to assess your situation and help you find the resources you will need to start your journey. Go to www.patriciadiesel.com/contact, fill in the form and I will contact you within 1-2 business days.

In Chapter 3, we will look at the steps that you can take to incorporate Clean Living into your body. You will be surprised at how these simple steps can make a substantial difference in your life!

Some chapters include the Vim & Vitality Action Checklist to develop additional, practical steps that you can take to make your journey into Clean Living a reality.

Vim & Vitality Action Checklist

✓ **How strong is your desire for a fresh, fit, forward life?**

1 2 3 4 5 6 7 8 9 10

✓ **Where are the areas you feel you need the most help? (Check all areas that apply)**

Body

☐ My health is good and I want to keep it that way
☐ I want to improve my general health
☐ I want to address a specific health issue

Mind

☐ I have a good mindset and I want to make it better
☐ I struggle with emotions like fear and I want to get rid of them
☐ My mindset is not healthy and I need to change

Environment

☐ My house is clean and tidy but I can always use tips to make it better
☐ It is a battle to keep things clean and I could use a system that works
☐ My house is a disaster and I don't know where to start

✓ **From your answers above, where is the most important place for you to start?** (If you are not sure or need help making that decision then please go to www.patriciadiesel.com/contact for your free 30-minute consultation.)

____

____

____

Chapter 3: It All Begins Here

Some people take better care of their car than they do of their body. Most people, in fact, pay little attention to their body until something goes wrong. Yet why create that kind of situation?

Look at what you are eating. How much and how often do you exercise? When was your last check-up? Are you treating your physical vehicle as if it is Divine? Good for you if you are. If you aren't...why not?

Neale Donald Walsch

Most of us strive to have a fit and nourished body with lots of energy to spare. Who doesn't want to look and feel good? The challenge is that it takes a combination of thought and action to make it happen. A fresh mindset is required if we are going to take responsibility for our wellness.

From a very early age, we have been conditioned in our thought processes. These thought processes include what we should eat and how we view our food and body. This conditioning includes our routines, which may or may not include physical exercise, implementing sound sleeping habits, and our ideas of how we should take care of ourselves.

It is important to recognize that we live in a different world from when we were very young. Our food today is heavily processed, and our crops are genetically engineered (GMO) and contain very few vital nutrients compared to 50 years ago.

Foods that our parents or grandparents grew up eating that kept them healthy now no longer meet our needs. What do we doif we can't follow what previous generations did?

The best thing we can do is take a proactive, preventative approach that wards off disease and inflammation before it starts. This isn't about a diet — it's about learning how to create a new lifestyle that suits your body. Awareness is the first step in the process of change. Here is a fun way to learn more about yourself and where you stand on this topic.

The Fit & Nourished Body Quiz

Answer each question on a scale of 1 to 10. Be honest with yourself. The point of this quiz is to see the areas you are doing well in and the areas that need improvement. When you are done, add up your score and we will look at the results.

1. If you knew that by eating and living clean you could extend your life by 10 years, would you adapt a new lifestyle?

1 2 3 4 5 6 7 8 9 10

2. How educated are you on pesticides on your food?

1 2 3 4 5 6 7 8 9 10

3. How informed are you on nutrition and what's healthy for you?

1 2 3 4 5 6 7 8 9 10

4. Do you get proper sleep and rest?

1 2 3 4 5 6 7 8 9 10

5. How often do you exercise?

1 2 3 4 5 6 7 8 9 10

6. If you could live well without prescription medications just by eating well and exercising properly, would you?

1 2 3 4 5 6 7 8 9 10

7. Do you know the difference between organic vs standard farm-raised food?

1 2 3 4 5 6 7 8 9 10

8. Would you choose to buy organic food over supermarket food?

1 2 3 4 5 6 7 8 9 10

9. How educated are you about GMOs in your food?

1 2 3 4 5 6 7 8 9 10

10. How often do you plan your meals?

1 2 3 4 5 6 7 8 9 10

Now add up your score out of ______ /100.

How did you do? If you scored below 50, then this is an area where you are going to want to focus your time and energy. If you scored 50-75, then you are on track. This chapter will help you take it to the next level. Above 75, then you have things well under control, BUT you still will want to read this chapter for additional information that might help you on your journey to Clean Living.

The 4 Components Of Great Health

Our bodies are complex machines. It is incredibly beautiful when you really think about how intricate of a structure we are. That each part of our body does its own unique job to ensure we run efficiently. It is the perfect example of synergy in motion for good health.

But…

It has specific needs if it is going to continue running well for 70-100 years. The rest of this chapter shares with you the four main components of good health. They are:

- Detoxing
- Alkaline Vs. Acidic Body
- Exercise
- Rest

Before we get into each one, there is one important concept to cover and that is awareness of what you are putting into your body. So many of us eat without being conscious of what effects it may have on our health.

When we get stressed we eat. When we are happy and celebrating we eat. When we feel sad or depressed we eat. When we are tired and bored we eat and/or reach for caffeine and sugar.

Over time, stress eating will eventually take a physical toll on our body and mind. While we *think* we are comforting ourselves with food with a temporary feeling of satisfaction, in the long run, eating the wrong food excessively can cause more harm than good. Before we know it, it becomes a vicious cycle that can be difficult to break.

So, what's the antidote?

Start with *intentional eating*. This is where we are not only aware of what we put into our bodies, but we also plan it. We take charge of meal and snack planning so that everyday we are receiving the nutrients we need for optimum health and strength.

These four areas are what made the difference in my health and are generally accepted as good practices to maintain a body properly but…

I can only share with you what worked for me. These are the things I did to improve my health. It is your responsibility to be your own medical advocate and detective.

What worked for me may not be exactly what you need. Do your research. Don't just take my word for it. Before I started anything, I spent a lot of time doing my homework. I only settled on a course of action once I KNEW for sure that it felt right for me!

Detoxing

Detoxing is a very misunderstood component of having a fit and nourished body. It is not an "easy escape route" so you can eat whatever you want and then purge it out later. Neither is it a quick way of losing weight so you can fit into that outfit for an important event you have.

Detoxing is an effective way to remove harmful materials such as waste and toxins from the body. Our bodies are constantly being bombarded with contaminants in our food, pollutants in the air, chemically filled medications and toxins that we use in our homes.

While we do have a natural detoxing system, all these contaminants overload our natural ability to get rid of unhealthy things so they end up being stored in our fat cells.

Even though our kidneys, lungs, skin and lymph nodes all help to detoxify the body, it is the liver that carries most of the load. It was never designed to be able to get rid of toxins at the levels we see today.

Over time, these elevated levels of toxins break down our bodies' immune systems and provide sickness and disease with a ripe environment for growth. When we detox, we take the stress off our vital organs and make it possible for them to do their job properly.

Alkaline Vs. Acid

Have you ever heard the term pH? If you are like most people you think of swimming pools and how much chlorine must be added to try and keep it clean. But pH is so much more than that. Did you know that our pH level plays an important part in our health? pH stands for potential of hydrogen and it indicates the level of acidity or alkalinity in something.

There are many areas where you find it, including our soil and our oceans. It is also a vital part of our health and most people don't even know that it exists in our bodies, let alone how it affects our health. pH is measured on a scale of 0 to 14. The number 7 is neutral. The lower the number below seven, the more acidic the substance is.

The higher the number is above seven, the substance is more alkaline.

A healthy human body fluid should sit at 7.4, which is slightly alkaline. A few areas, like the stomach, are very acidic, but most of the body should be alkaline. It only takes a small amount of acidity over a prolonged period of time to see deterioration.

Here is the issue: most of us have acidic bodies. When our bodies have a pH under 7, it ages us faster, puts more stress on our vital organs, we lose tissue and bone mass, and it robs our body of vital nutrients.

The Solution

The simplest way to combat the damage of acidic pH levels is to design an organic food plan that is high in alkaline and limits foods that produce acid in the body. Organic foods boost alkalinity and energy production. I love the way Dr. Henele explains organic in his book, *Energetic Health: Interesting Insights Into Advanced Natural Medicine.* He explains that:

> *"Organic foods are a great way to support alkalinity in your bloodstream and inside*

your cells. Organic foods are superior to conventional foods because they have a higher nutrient density, a higher antioxidant potential, and they are usually farmed in humane and sustainable ways. You get all of this without environmental pollution and bacterial infections. Every dollar spent on organic foods is a vote cast for your future. When you choose organic foods, you choose life."

Organic foods do not contain pesticides. These toxins get trapped in the body for many years, especially if you have weight problems. Pesticides can cause problems in your nervous system, your heart, immune system and lungs.

Have you ever noticed the shelf life of an organically grown fruit versus conventionally grown fruit? Usually, the organic fruit goes bad within days; it will show outward signs of rotting and have an odor while the conventional fruit does not. What's keeping the conventional fruit lasting this long? Pesticides and preservatives. Is this what we really want to ingest into our bodies? For me, I didn't have to think twice about switching to organic.

Remember: Any food that contains pesticides, preservatives, GMOs and other chemicals will have an acidic nature.

The Health Benefits Of An Alkaline Diet

It is fascinating to see how many health conditions are linked to not having the proper pH balance in the body. By simply raising your pH, you can see considerable improvements in your health. Some conditions include:

- **Pain and inflammation** including headaches, muscle spasms, lower back pain, menstrual symptoms and joint pain
- **Cardiovascular health** in conjunction with high blood pressure and cholesterol, kidney stones and stroke
- **Bone density** and muscle mass
- **Magnesium deficiency**

What Does An Alkaline Food Plan Look Like?

There are contrasting schools of thought on the best way to alkalize your body. Every "body" is distinctive and reacts differently as people tolerate certain foods better than others. You have to find what works best for you. This list gives suggestions and acts as a template to introduce some of the top picks.

- It starts with fresh organic fruits and vegetables: kale, cucumbers, celery, broccoli, endive, spinach, peppers, green beans, carrots, cabbage, cauliflower, avocado, apples, bananas, watermelon, lemons, oranges.
- Eat your vegetables raw or slightly steamed at most. Why raw foods? There is a presence of a beneficial antioxidant, quercetin, that is found in fruits and vegetables. You can also juice them. If this concept is new to you, then try it at least one day per week to give it a whirl.

Remember: Hard boiling and deep frying removes most of the nutrients, including quercetin.

- Start eating plant proteins. These will help to make you feel full and provide you with an additional source of fiber. Quinoa, chia seed, flax seed, hemp seed, are all excellent sources of plant proteins.
- Drink plenty of alkaline water. Most tap

water and even bottled water is acidic. You can test the pH levels of your tap water using a kit purchased through your local health food, aquarium or pool supply store. Do your research on the bottled water available in your area.

➢ Drink Green. You can do this with smoothies or by juicing. Rich, green vegetables are known to contain chlorophyll. Chlorophyll has a similar structure as our blood, which is good for balancing and alkalizing the blood. Greens associated with high levels of chlorophyll are chlorella, kale, spinach and collard greens.

The following food groups are known to cause acidity and have little nutritional value for you. I understand it can be difficult to break some of those habits, so if you continue consuming these foods, try to do so in moderation.

➢ Pasta, rice, bread

➢ Processed cereals

➢ Coffee, tea and alcohol

➢ Soda/Soft Drinks

➢ Milk (Did you know that we are the only species of mammals that consumes milk after infancy and drink another species' milk?)

Some great alternatives include almond and coconut milk.

- Eggs
- Conventional meats and cold cuts
- Any food high in salt (which includes most processed foods)
- All grains including wheat, oats and corn

Remember: Clean Living is about making minor changes over a gradual period of time. You can do your homework and figure out a food plan that works for you and improves your health. Not everyone needs to be on a vegan diet. These are the things I had to get rid of so I could live healthy.

ꕥ

Madison's Story

As Madison neared retirement, she realized that she needed to make some changes in her life. She was overweight and was starting to notice symptoms of certain illnesses coming upon her.

She also realized just how much clutter she had in her home when she decided to relocate back to her home town. She wanted to be closer to her roots and spend time with her family, but the thought of getting her house packed up was daunting, to say the least. She also knew that physically it would be hard for her to even TRY.

She contacted me and we started working on one area at a time. First, we looked at her food choices and I encouraged her to make some changes. She purchased a blender and a juicer and learned where to get organic food in her area.

As she started to feel better physically, it

was time to work on her environment. We implemented a game plan that she could manage, which included action steps that she looked forward to completing.

Within a matter of months, not only was Madison feeling better, but she was also able to make the move back to her home town. She is now happily living in an apartment that makes her feel great and is spending time with the people she loves.

Exercise

Of course, everybody knows exercise is part of healthy living, yet it is one of those words that most of us dread. I have heard very few people in my lifetime wake up and say, "Yes! I get to exercise today!" But the benefits to exercise are amazing.

Regular exercise will keep your bones strong, increase your body's flexibility, improve muscle strength, boost your endurance, help deliver oxygen and nutrients to your tissues, and strengthen your cardiovascular system.

The main thing is to find a healthy exercise regimen that fits into your lifestyle. If your girlfriend is out there riding her bike every day, and bicycling just isn't your thing, don't do it.

Find something that you really look forward to doing. Go take a dance class or try yoga. If you are not sure, then experiment, but find something.

Always start off slowly with exercise, then build on it. Over time, you will reap the benefits of exercise and you will be so glad you did.

And finally ...

Rest

Adequate sleep is a key part of healthy living. Most people don't realize the power that sleep has. Sleep not only makes you feel better, but it also boosts and protects us in more ways than one. Some of the major benefits to a good night's rest include:

- Protects brain function
- Helps you learn
- Repairs your heart and blood vessels
- Helps keep your weight down
- Keeps your hormones balanced
- Promotes proper insulin levels
- Helps children and teens grow

What's Next?

By planning your health, you can live a full, long life. It is important to seek out professional help. I highly suggest that you seek out a nutritionist or doctor of naturopathic medicine to help you make these changes. Consult your local listings for one near you.

In the next chapter, we are going to look at the power of your mind in living a vibrant life. Make sure you check out the Vim & Vitality Checklist on the next page to help start you on your journey to good physical health.

Vim & Vitality Action Checklist

✓ **On a scale of 1 to 10, how would you rate your self-care?**

1 2 3 4 5 6 7 8 9 10

✓ **What foods are you going to incorporate into your daily routine?**

- ☐ Organic Fruits
- ☐ Organic Vegetables
- ☐ Quinoa
- ☐ Flax & Chia Seeds
- ☐ Alkaline Water
- ☐ Green Drinks
- ☐ Juice Drinks

✓ **Are you willing to commit to paying attention to what goes in your mouth when stressed?**

- ☐ **Yes**
- ☐ **No**

✓ **Are you willing to commit to doing research to find the best way to detoxify your body?**

- ☐ **Yes**
- ☐ **No**

✓ **What types of exercise are you going to implement in your life?**

____

✓ **Are you willing to commit to getting the proper sleep each night?**

- ☐ **Yes**
- ☐ **No**

Chapter 4: Powerful Brain Cycles

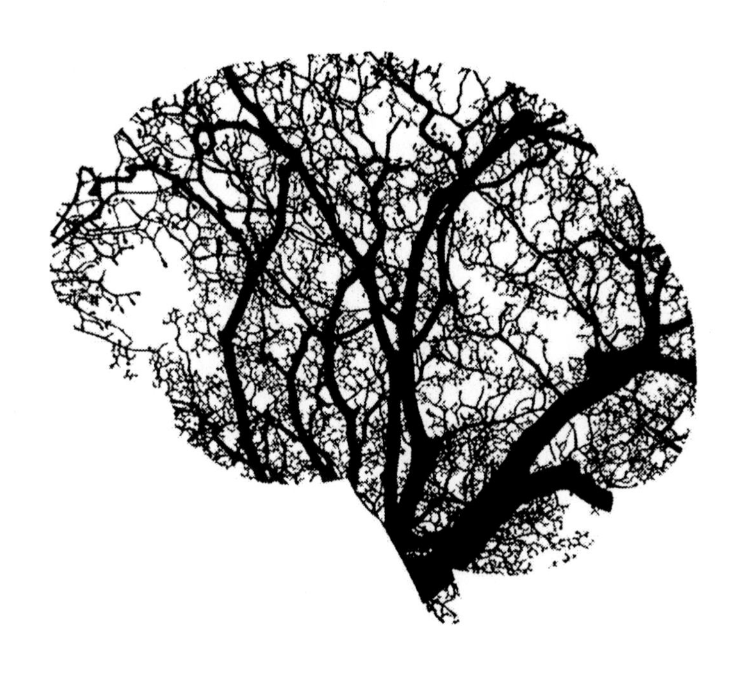

If you change the way you look at things, the things you look at change.

Wayne Dyer

Tammy's life always felt like a struggle where nothing good ever happened. She couldn't understand how her sister's life was filled with happy, positive things and hers wasn't.

For example, the other morning when Tammy woke up from a bad night's sleep (because her co-worker had ticked her off so much that she couldn't get it out of her mind), she was already grouchy. Her kids weren't in a good mood either (maybe because the first thing she did was yell at them) and they were moving slowly.

Everything seemed to take forever. She couldn't find her blouse or the shoes that she wanted to wear, her three-year-old spilled milk all over her new pants, and her 10-year-old told Tammy that she needed to bring snacks in for her class that day. That was only the beginning of her problems!

The car started to act funny on the way to work and Tammy realized that she was way overdue for the oil change. The air conditioning no longer worked in her car so by the time she arrived at work, perspiration marks were showing through her blouse. To top it off, she was running late for an important meeting.

All these things turned her bad mood into a horrible one, and the meeting reflected it. What Tammy didn't know was that this meeting was a test, deliberately scheduled to see how well she performed under pressure because Tammy was being considered for a promotion.

As one might expect, she didn't get the position. On the way home, all Tammy could think of was every negative thing that had ever happened in her life…

The next morning, she got a call from her sister Lisa. Lisa was bubbling over with excitement about the raise she had just gotten. Tammy tried to be pleasant and supportive over the phone, but on the inside, she was seething with resentment. *Why do good things always happen to Lisa, while I always get the short end of the stick? It just isn't fair!*

This thought led Tammy to thinking about Lisa's elegant home and how it is always neat and tidy compared to Tammy's disaster area. *It was enough to make a person sick!*

As she pondered these thoughts, Tammy started to realize that Lisa has always had a positive attitude. *It doesn't seem to matter what happens. Lisa handles it with ease and looks for the good in all situations.*

Maybe it's time Tammy finds out more about healthy thinking. It certainly couldn't hurt...

How Cluttered Is Your Brain?

There are days when anyone can feel mentally overwhelmed. It happens. But when your whole life feels like a constant state of overwhelm, it's time to pay attention. A cluttered, stress-filled brain can make life feel like a continual struggle. Peace of mind seems out of reach.

Not sure how cluttered your brain is? Try the quiz below to find out where you stand. Pick the one answer that best fits your usual mental state.

1. How often do you feel stressed?

a) Never b) Seldom

c) Most days d) Every day

2. How often do you lose your temper?

a) Never b) Seldom

c) Most days d) Every day

3. When a problem occurs, how often is your first reaction to look for a solution?

a) Always b) Occasionally

c) Seldom d) Never

4. Do you find it hard to fall asleep because your brain won't shut down?

a) Never b) Seldom

c) Most days d) Every day

5. Do you feel road rage when you drive?

a) Never

b) Seldom

c) Most days

d) Every day

6. How do you feel most days?

a) Happy & content

b) Content

c) Slightly negative

d) Negative

7. How well do you focus on tasks?

a) Great, no problems

b) Occasionally have problems

c) Most days it's hard

d) I can never focus

8. How clean and organized is your house, office, desk and car?

a) Always clean & organized

b) Occasionally messy

c) Messy, but cleanable in a few hours

d) Never clean

9. How would people describe you?

a) Optimistic

b) Mostly optimistic

c) Occasionally pessimistic

d) Debbie or Donny Downer

10. How hopeful are you that life keeps on getting better and better?

a) Always hopeful

b) Mostly hopeful

c) Sometimes hopeful

d) Never hopeful

Now, count how many of each letter you have:

a) _____ b) _____ c) _____ d) _____

Mostly A's

You are an extremely happy, positive person who has a good outlook on life. You know how to deal with the stressful situations that life brings. This chapter will give you fascinating insight into your own good "mental health habits" and strengthen the coping skills you have already developed.

Mostly B's

You are in a good place most days and generally feel balanced, but when the pressure is on, things can quickly fly out of control. Wouldn't it feel great to know that you can be depended upon to handle the crisis days when they come along? Look for suggestions throughout this chapter that will show you how.

Mostly C's

You struggle more often than you like to admit. Does it feel like you "just aren't lucky?" It may seem like life has you on the ropes much of the time, but you still have hope that your life will improve. You know that you are a fighter. Now is the time to turn it around! This chapter will help you understand how to harness your thought patterns better and work towards a more balanced life.

Mostly D's

You struggle daily with your thoughts. As far as you are concerned, the world has it in for you, and hope is something other people have. This is affecting the quality of your life! This is a serious health issue, and I strongly encourage you to read this chapter and reach out for professional support. Learn to understand your thought patterns better and work towards a more positive outlook. Your future depends on it!

How Does A Cluttered Brain Play Out In Life?

Studies show that when our brain is cluttered, we can experience overload. Think of it like a circuit board that shorts out. Our brains are capable of holding only so much information at any given time. Experiencing this overload for an extended period will eventually take a toll on our physical and emotional well-being.

The effects of exhaustion can ultimately influence other areas of our lives. Exhaustion makes it more difficult to perform at our best or to maintain the quality of our relationships. If we are never fully rested, all aspects of our lives will gradually deteriorate.

When we are approaching an overloaded state, we can begin to display negative behaviors. These actions are clues to alert us to the fact we are losing control. Some indicators that you are reaching overload capacity are:

- Isolation
- Unhappiness
- Blaming others
- Under achievement
- Toxic relationships
- Cluttered house
- Little or no patience
- Feelings of regret

Healthy Vs. Unhealthy Thought Patterns

Think of your brain like a computer designed to run machinery. You program a computer with a series of commands and it will act accordingly. If the command codes are good, things run well and much is accomplished — a product is successfully produced.

If the command codes are bad, the product comes out faulty, unsellable. There is the strong possibility that the machine will damage itself in the process! The mind works the same way. Good programming creates positive thoughts. Bad programming creates negative thoughts.

A Simple Exercise

Here is a great exercise to figure out how your internal programming is affecting you. Throughout the day, periodically write down your thoughts. Then place a P for Positive or N for Negative next to it.

At the end of the day, take time to review what you wrote. Do you see a connection between the way your day went and the nature of your thoughts? An event might truly be neutral, but the way you frame your response to it will have lasting impact on your day. Consider how you framed your day, and whether it is part of a larger pattern.

Understanding Our Brains

When we understand how the brain works, it makes it easier for us to shift our thinking. To recap, we know that positive and negative thoughts influence our brain.

In a study conducted by the Journal of Clinical Psychology, researchers examined how worrying (which is a form of negative thinking) affects people's ability to sort objects.

People who worried more than 50% of the time could perform the easy tasks, but as the challenge level increased, the harder it became for them to focus and complete the task.

The people who were positive minded could progress much further and perform more challenging tasks. In conclusion, the study revealed that negative thinking makes it harder to think clearly and process information. It also affected decision-making and problem-solving skills.

Let's look at how the brain functions and how negative thoughts hinder everyday life.

The Amygdala

The amygdala is a structure located deep in the brain. It is responsible for several processes. First, it stores memories and second, it controls the mind's "flight or fight" response.

Can you see where that might not be a good combination? Back in the times when we needed a "flight or fight" response for survival, remembering negative consequences of an action could mean the difference between life and death. But…

In the modern world, we rarely have that problem anymore. We do not spend each day wondering if we will be attacked by wild animals or if we will freeze to death because we do not have enough wood. At most, we might think about having a car accident when someone slams on their brakes in front of us.

When our brains are full of negative thoughts, it keeps our amygdala active. This trains our bodies to respond to every situation as though they are massive problems that hinder us from living life, even things that should be easy to handle. It also signals other parts of the brain that stress is happening, which leads us to the…

Thalamus

The thalamus takes the signals it gets from other parts of the brain and relays them to the body. When we have a sudden fright, it is our thalamus that signals our heart to beat faster and makes us feel anxious. It is also responsible for our flight response.

Here is the problem: the thalamus cannot tell the difference between a real threat and an imagined threat created by negative thoughts. In both cases, the system has an automatic response to the perceived threat. This creates a dangerous loop: the more negative thoughts we have, the more stress we feel.

What Stress Does

Stress may be the culprit to many health-related problems. For example, that nagging headache, reoccurring insomnia or decline in productivity can be blamed on on-going stress.When left untreated, constant stress can lead to a whole host of problems. Indeed, stress can affect your body, mind and environment.

ꕥ

Cassidy's Story

Cassidy is a beautiful, creative woman who had suffered a great loss. Her husband of many years had passed away tragically and she was having a hard time getting over it.

She spent most of her time watching TV in an attempt to numb her pain. This numbness made it difficult for Cassidy to confront her deep grief and she became more and more depressed.

She had been to doctors and therapists, but they hadn't been able to help her. The medication they gave her only delayed the inevitable. Even the things that brought her joy, such as pottery making, went to the wayside.

Cassidy reached out to me to see if there was a way that I could help her as a coach. Her relationships had started to suffer, especially her relationship with her adult married son, and she wasn't sure why.

In our sessions, I realized that she was developing negative mental habits that were hurting both Cassidy and her son. These negative habits were keeping her in a very painful place. She missed her husband so much that she was expecting her son to take his father's place emotionally.

She wanted her son to take care of her and be there for her, in the way her husband had always done when he was alive. Of course, her son couldn't do that. He was married with a family, and dealing with his own grief of losing his father.

Cassidy didn't want to deal with the grief in her heart because she felt it was too hard. So, she tried to find a replacement instead. The problem is that no one could replace her husband. Cassidy now needed to learn how to let go.

As our coaching continued, Cassidy was able to accept this and in time begin the grieving process. Eventually she was able to get back to the things she enjoyed and pursue her pottery again.

The Process Of Changing Your Thoughts

For many people, learning how to change unhealthy thought patterns may be the hardest thing they ever do. Remember how we discussed how repeated thoughts can create a neural pathway, a "groove" in our minds? The longer the negative thought patterns have been in place, the harder it becomes to change them. But there is hope. The more we want to change, the easier it will be.

Make The Choice

Choice involves decision making. We can choose to live a certain way or we can choose not to. We may *want* to change, but when it comes down to actually implementing change, we can fall short. We choose to change because the old way is no longer serving us. We realize that the benefits of change will far outweigh the old.

Change empowers us and puts us in a positive mindset. It is amazing what happens in our brains when we do this. Think of it as our brains getting rewired. The good news is that every time we choose to think positively, it gets easier until it forms into a habit that gets cemented in our brain.

Awareness

Remember that thought-tracking exercise we did earlier where we wrote down our thoughts during the day? Now is the time to put it to good use. There is a formula I want to teach you:

NT ➢ NE ➢ NR ➢ NRE

NT = Negative Thoughts

NE = Negative Emotions

NR = Negative Reactions

NRE = Negative Results

When you have negative thoughts, it causes you to have negative emotions. Those emotions shape your reactions. When those reactions are negative it creates a bad result.

For example, someone says something that you don't like. Your first thought is, "What right do you have to say that to me?" This puts you in a bad mood. Because of the way you feel, you say something nasty to your boss and the result is you now have a black mark on your work record.

So, the first step in breaking that cycle is to become aware of your negative thoughts. Once you are aware that they are there, you can change them into positive ones.

Switching Your Thoughts

Now comes the fun part, switching our thoughts. Here is where the real work begins. Every time we have a negative thought we need to replace it with a positive one.

"But what if I don't believe the positive thought?" Good question. It doesn't matter. Make the choice to think the opposite of that negative thought.

For example, you may just have stubbed your toe and the first thought in your head is, "I always stub my toe." Recognize the thought and replace it with, "That is the last time I will stub my toe." You may not believe that yet in your heart but by choosing to think "that is the last time,"over time you will train your awareness to avoid potential problems in the future.

Here's a great exercise you can do.

Make a commitment to yourself to CHOOSE to go one full day without saying anything negative in your life. Challenge yourself. At first, you may catch yourself falling back into some old thought patterns. That's okay. Make a mental note of it, reprogram it with a positive thought and move forward. It is a process and it does take time, but it is worth the effort.

Remember: Anything worth doing takes time. Eventually you will start to notice significant change in your attitude and how your days play out.

Change Your Brainwaves

Our brain cells use electricity to communicate thoughts and regulate our bodies. Different electrical frequencies are associated with various mental states. Some promote positivity and others don't. It is important that we work with our brain's natural systems to make the process easier.

Some of the ways we can change brain frequency is through meditation, prayer and affirmations. These three practices can activate and "rewire" the brain to allow the frequency to change to a higher vibration, a positive one.

More Tips To Help You

We must be cautious about listening to the inner voice in our heads as we go about our day. It can be a constant monologue that either builds us up or tears us down. The voice that builds us up is a friend that we need to listen to. The inner voice that tears us down is an enemy in disguise that needs to be kicked to the curb for good.

What does "the one who breaks us down" sound like? You will hear that voice in these words.

- I can't
- You'll never
- It's impossible

That voice always has bad news. *"I blew it again. What a failure."* When that inner voice tells us that "we can't do it" or "we can't make it," that inner voice must be fought and conquered. This takes awareness and making deliberate choices about our thoughts.

Some people may find that they have listened to that voice for so long that they don't know how to get rid of it. That is where coaching comes in. I love working with people to create a plan that works for them. Interested? Go to www.patriciadiesel.com/contact and fill out the form for us to spend some time together.

Another technique to develop a positive mindset is to build up a "greatest hits playlist" of positive thoughts by speaking these thoughts aloud. Our brains tend to believe what we hear. If you want to reinforce new patterns, this will help do it faster.

Think of it like a musician preparing for a concert. Try it out in the shower or in the car on the drive to work. Unless you carpool… I don't expect you to look crazy in front of other people by talking to yourself!

The words that you say to yourself matter. Try to avoid negative words like "always," "never," "should," and "must." If we find ourselves saying things like, "I'm always late," this only strengthens the habit of giving up our power and cast ourselves in the role of victim. Instead you can say, "Today, I will not be late." Choose words that empower rather than weaken.

Our imaginations can get away from us. A late bus, a spilled coffee or a missed phone call are simply inconveniences, not catastrophes. Look at situations realistically and not based on past experiences.

Remember: We do have the power to change our thoughts and change our life.

I hope that you enjoyed this chapter and have come to realize that when you change your thoughts, you can change your life. If you still feel stuck and would like some additional help, I am here for you. Go to www.patriciadiesel.com/contact, fill out the form and I will connect with you for a free 30-minute consultation to help you get started.

Vim & Vitality Action Checklist

✓ Did you do the cluttered brain quiz at the beginning of the chapter? What was your result?

____

____

✓ On a scale of 1 to 10, how positive is your thinking?

1 2 3 4 5 6 7 8 9 10

✓ Are you dealing with any of these things?

- ☐ Unfulfilled dreams
- ☐ No peace
- ☐ Bad relationships
- ☐ Little to few friends
- ☐ A messy house
- ☐ Always blaming others
- ☐ Not taking responsibility

✓ Have you realized that your thought patterns need to change?

- ☐ **Yes**
- ☐ **No**

✓ Are you willing to commit to the steps required to make the change?

- ☐ **Yes**
- ☐ **No**

Chapter 5:
Smart Living

For every minute spent organizing,
an hour is earned.

Benjamin Franklin

So far, we have covered two of the three main concepts for Clean Living. We looked at our physical bodies in Chapter 3 and how we can take our health to the next level. In Chapter 4, we looked at emotional detoxifying and how to clear our mental clutter and turn to positive thinking. Now, we will look at how our environment affects our lives.

Why apply the Clean Living principle to your environment? Living in a clean, fresh, pure and smart environment will rejuvenate and restore you after your day. Home becomes an intimate sacred space that meets your physical needs and your mental and spiritual ones as well.

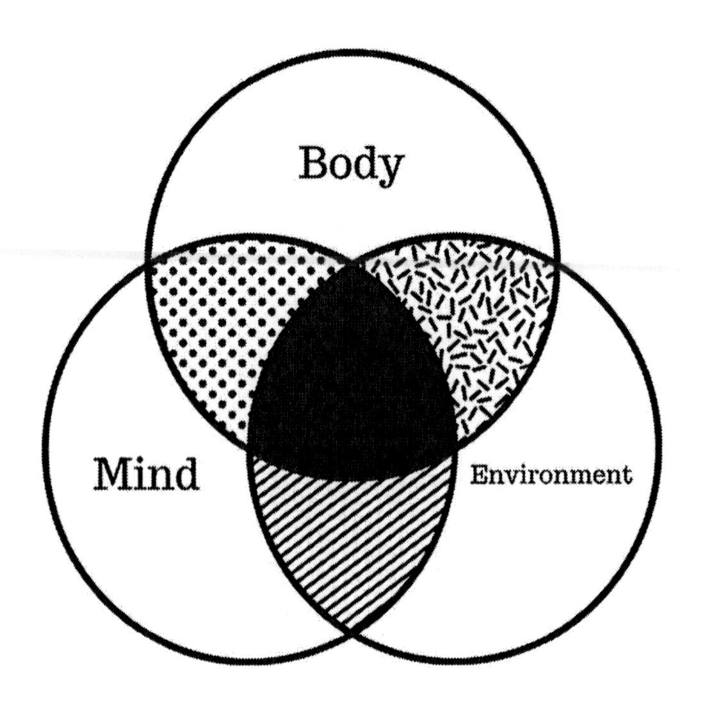
Body
Mind
Environment

The Smart Living Quiz

Most people are unsure if their environment is affecting them or not. Take this fun quiz and see how well you do. Answer each question on a scale of 1 to 10 and add the score at the end. Are you ready? Let's go.

1. Would you consider your house clean? Choose 1 for "No way, not even close," and 10 for "My house is perfect. I could have the Queen of England in for tea."

1 2 3 4 5 6 7 8 9 10

2. I devote time every day to keeping my house tidy.

1 2 3 4 5 6 7 8 9 10

3. I use cleaners that do not add toxins to my home.

1 2 3 4 5 6 7 8 9 10

4. I have lots of plants to clean the air and produce oxygen.

1 2 3 4 5 6 7 8 9 10

5. I can declutter when things start to pile up.

1 2 3 4 5 6 7 8 9 10

6. My house is filled with beautiful things that make me feel peaceful.

1 2 3 4 5 6 7 8 9 10

7. I have no problems when people show up at my door unannounced.

1 2 3 4 5 6 7 8 9 10

8. I don't let clutter get to the point where I feel overwhelmed.

1 2 3 4 5 6 7 8 9 10

9. Everything in my house has its own designated place.

1 2 3 4 5 6 7 8 9 10

10. I have a system in place for daily and weekly cleaning.

1 2 3 4 5 6 7 8 9 10

Now add up your score out of ______ /100.

How did you do? Many people are surprised by their results. If your score is 71 or higher, congratulations! You are crafting a nurturing environment that will increase a Clean Living lifestyle.

If your score is 51-70, there is still some work that needs to be done to properly support a life centered around Clean Living. If your score is under 50, then this is an area that is going to need serious attention to help you see the change you want in your life.

What Does A Cluttered Home Look Like?

An important observation for me to emphasize is that how one chooses to live *is a very personal choice.* A person who lives in a cluttered home may consider it to be "eclectic" whereas another person may think "Get me out of here!" What matters most is the comfort level of the homeowner.

Everyone is messy from time to time, but when it starts to interfere with the quality of a person's life, then that becomes a different issue. For example, there is a substantial difference between messy, chronically disorganized and hoarding.

Each of these problems can leave a person feeling overwhelmed and stressed, but when our environment threatens our well-being, as in the case of hoarding, it is time for professional help.

I like to live in a very neat, clean and organized space. My house reflects that. I must confess, when it does get a little messy, it makes me feel off-kilter and distracted. But that's me. I like to deal with my "stuff" right away and don't feel comfortable with clutter or mess around me.

My friend Deborah, on the other hand, has a more relaxed view and is quite comfortable with a house that has a "lived in" feel. Most times, things will get put away, but if it takes a day or two, it doesn't bother her. It doesn't make either one of us wrong or right — it is a personal preference. What works for one may not work for another.

There are some indicators to watch out for so you know when it's time to begin the decluttering process. One is frustration. Imagine how you feel when you can't find your things. We have all been there before. By contrast, consider how peaceful you feel when you can locate your car keys, or checkbook at a moment's notice, without wasting time.

Another indicator that it is time to declutter is when your possessions do not have a permanent place in your home. The golden rule is, "A place for everything, and everything in its proper place." Everything you own must have a home. If not, you can bank on the clutter hanging around your home *forever*. Because the longer you procrastinate in dealing with clutter, the more difficult it becomes to control.

ꟾ

Cynthia's Story

Cynthia had a bittersweet childhood. Her mother died of cancer when Cynthia was four years old. Cynthia and her sister were raised by their father, David. He was a good man who loved his two daughters and did the best he could to raise them right. They made many wonderful memories together.

But…

There was one area in particular where David struggled to teach his daughters: basic housekeeping skills. He worked hard and endured a daily two-hour commute to earn the money to supply for the physical needs of his daughters.

When he got home at night and on the weekends, he didn't have the energy to clean. In reality, he didn't know how to clean, either. So, "disaster zone" was the typical state of their home.

When Cynthia grew up and began life as a young wife and mother, she was completely overwhelmed by it all. It was not long before her home was a disaster zone that bordered on hoarding.

The good news was that Cynthia wasn't too emotionally attached to the things in her home. She just didn't have the systems in place to keep it organized, so clutter just kept piling up.

Thankfully, she knew that she needed to look for help! I helped her get rid of the clutter and gave her the organizational and cleaning skills that she needed to keep it in better shape.

Now, is Cynthia's home perfect? No, but now she can easily get it into presentable shape in a couple of hours, instead of the two weeks it used to take her when company was expected.

❧

Where Does The Clutter Come From?

There are many reasons why "things" can get out of hand. Life has a way of throwing curve balls. Circumstances can change in an instant, creating a crisis that can leave a person without the time or energy to deal with housekeeping. These are unfortunate situations.

A possible solution would be to hire a professional organizer to help out. The extra support eases the burden and allows for the family to deal with more important tasks.

One of the main reasons that a person's environment gets cluttered is the same reason that Cynthia had. They just never learned certain life skills. For example:

- How does someone make a bed in the morning?
- How is dirty laundry taken care of?
- What is the right way to clean up after a meal?
- How is a bathroom kept clean and fresh?

These are all teachable skill sets. Without these skill sets in an organized system, the individual is left to "make it up as they go along," usually making things more complicated than necessary and causing undue stress! In this chapter, we will discuss the process of decluttering one's life.

The Benefits Of Decluttering

There's a certain connotation the word declutter brings to mind — don't you think? For me it evokes a feeling of freedom. By now, I am sure you know that I personally do not operate well when I have clutter around me.

So, anything I can do to get myself on track quickly helps not just with my immediate surroundings, but it also makes my mind clearer and focused. My attitude starts to shift and I feel more energy.

Let's look at three good reasons why decluttering is healthy:

1. You Can Decrease Stress

Not having clutter around reduces your worry and anxiety. Next time you have unannounced guests, you don't have to fret and scramble to hide things before letting them in. Just knowing your place is environmentally friendly is a load off the old noggin.

2. You Can Breathe Easier

Regular household dust is enough to deal with. But excessive clutter may contain mold, and other toxins that can complicate health issues further, especially if you have asthma or other breathing problems.

3. You Can Clear Your Mind

Did you know that clutter can actually interfere with your brain's ability to process information? Think about it. Clutter is akin to chaos. Studies have proven that chaos restricts our ability to focus. When we are in a clutter-free space we experience more energy and productivity.

How To Declutter

To start decluttering, it is helpful to prepare yourself ahead of time as best as possible. Preparation is key. Think about what you are going to need to set yourself up for maximum efficiency and productivity.

Gather all your tools first. You will need: bins, boxes, trash bags, label maker, markers and a shredder. You don't want to have to interrupt your work just to hunt down tools as you need them. If you don't have a shredder, you can label a box "to shred." Many office supply stores offer shredding services for a nominal fee.

Start out after eating a nourishing meal. Gather plenty of water and a few healthy snacks. It's easy to get distracted when you're hungry or dehydrated, so inoculate yourself from this temptation ahead of time.

Shut off cell phones, television and computers. Put on some music. Select a pop radio station or pick music that fits your mood at the time. A good rule of thumb is to match the music to your personal energy level, but sometimes it is necessary to play music that will shift your energy.

For example, if you are feeling energized and peppy, don't play slow, mellow music. On the other hand, if you are feeling mellow, play something that will give you energy.

Determine how much time will be allotted for the decluttering session, and stick to your time, *whether you finish or not.* This is critical, as you don't want to have overwhelming exhaustion set in.

Setting an end time can be difficult to determine on your own, especially if you have difficulty with following through and setting priorities for yourself. Make it easy on yourself and set a timer for 15 minutes at a time. Each session will get you closer to your goal of Clean Living.

If you require assistance with this, you can get help by going to www.patriciadiesel.com/contact and request your free 30-minute consultation.

Going through your stuff might sound scary at first. The very idea can conjure up thoughts of dread — after all, if tossing stuff out was easy, you wouldn't have clutter! Pick a room and begin along one wall. As you examine your possessions and your clutter, ask yourself questions such as:

- What needs to be tossed?
- What needs to be kept?
- What needs to go back in its home?

To help you determine which category to assign to an object, I would like to teach you a game called: "Friend, Stranger, Acquaintance," that I learned from my mentor, Judith Kolberg. As you begin to declutter a room, give everything a name.

"Friends" are the items that we want to keep. These things deserve a proper place in our homes. Take your "friend" possessions and put them away in their assigned spots, e.g., pens go in a holder near the computer, the tv remote on the end table by your favorite chair, etc.

"Strangers" are the items that no longer serve us and should be released. "Released" can mean tossed, shredded or given away. Ad mail, old magazines, sample products and other "free" bonus gifts with purchase fall into this category. If you pick up something and find yourself asking, "Why do I have *this*?" it's time to start singing, "Please Release Me, Let Me Go!"

Things that are to be tossed, shredded or donated need to be taken care of right away. Don't just put them in a corner and leave them there for the next six months. Get them out of your home as quickly as possible.

The "Acquaintance" category is for items that have some sentimental meaning to you, like a gift from a well-meaning relative or a purchase that was expensive at the time. You might think, "I am not sure. I shouldn't throw it away; Aunt Edna gave me that. Maybe I could donate it to someone or maybe I will keep it. I'm just not sure where it goes yet."

If you haven't used it in the past six months, let it be a blessing to someone else, instead of a burden on you. Aunt Edna did not give you a gift to make you feel guilty!

The goal of decluttering is to clear out your space so you can begin to set your environment up for Clean Living. It's time to live in an environment where you can come home and rejuvenate and rest. Craft your intimate sacred space to nurture your whole self: physical, mental and spiritual.

❧

Obstacles You May Face

Once you have the tools, decluttering sounds easy, right? Not always. Sometimes, during this process, we can unearth unexpected memories, which can be very emotional. Old photographs, music and art can trigger an old memory of trauma like a romantic break-up or divorce, a loss of a career, an empty nest or the loss of a loved one.

Grief, deep grief, can make the decluttering process especially painful. Sometimes a grieving person will choose to declutter ruthlessly in an attempt to remove the pain caused by loss. *Better to have empty room than to face a constant reminder of what I lost.*

Mentally, they decide that it would be preferable to have it gone, in a sort of "emotional amputation." For others, they are simply not ready. When they try to get rid of something that belongs to the loved one, it is like that person is dying all over again.

If you are grieving, please be compassionate with yourself.

Finally, there is a phenomenon called Kinetic Sympathy coined by Judith Kolberg. She describes it as:

> *"Touching a thing can set off an emotional response. Perhaps the touching of a thing changes a simple act of throwing out into an emotional act of letting go."*

If you feel that this is an obstacle that you are facing then the best solution is to get support.

One of my clients was a professional actor who owned an amazing wardrobe of gorgeous costumes. Once she had retired from performing, she was having a challenging time parting with her costumes. She couldn't do it. If it had been a few outfits it wouldn't have been an issue but she had racks and racks of them lying around.

Through coaching, I helped her to understand that she was mourning her past life. She had to make peace with the life that she was in now, and look at it from a place of gratitude.

She could reflect on that time and remember she enjoyed blessings and opportunities that many people never get to experience, but living in the past was no longer serving her.

This fresh point of view helped my client realize that her past was hindering her future. She found a great way to let go of those costumes by donating them to a struggling local theatre and she made a powerful difference in the lives of up-and-coming performers.

Commitment is the key to successful decluttering. A wise course of action is to determine wholeheartedly *at the outset* to release things that no longer have a place in your life. It makes it easier to deal with the emotional side of the purging once this commitment has been made, because you are making the decision once and for all, rather than reassessing and deciding the fate of every object you touch.

Similarly, commitment is needed to make the process a priority. This eliminates the reasons (excuses) why decluttering projects remain incomplete. To avoid this from happening, schedule time in your calendar — just as if you were going to a very important meeting.

Show up for yourself like you would for any other appointment.

WOW! I can't believe that we are almost done. What a journey it has been. Clean Living has changed my life and a big part of that has been having a fresh, free environment using smart living concepts. When I come home, I enjoy a sense of peace in my sacred space and have an inviting environment to share with my family and friends. Using the ideas in this chapter, you can too.

Vim & Vitality Action Checklist

✓ When you come home and look around, how does it make you feel?

____

____

✓ On a scale of 1 to 10, how cluttered is your home? (1 is "very cluttered", 10 is "pristine")

1 2 3 4 5 6 7 8 9 10

✓ Do you feel ready to make changes in your environment?

- ☐ **Yes**
- ☐ **No**

✓ Do you have these things available to declutter your home?

- ☐ boxes
- ☐ bins
- ☐ tape
- ☐ markers
- ☐ trash bags
- ☐ labels
- ☐ shredder

✓ Have you set aside an appointment to declutter?

- ☐ **Yes**
- ☐ **No**

✓ Have you committed yourself to release sentimental items?

- ☐ **Yes**
- ☐ **No**

Chapter 6:
A Brand-New Start

Every new beginning comes from
some other beginning's end.

Seneca

"I don't think that I can be any happier than I am in this moment." Have you ever experienced that perfect moment in time that you want to stay in forever? It's like Heaven allowed you to feel complete and tranquil for that brief second.

What if you could live a life at peace within yourself and experience those moments on a regular basis? That is what Clean Living is all about: creating a synergetic ambiance between your body, mind and environment where all the components are in harmony with each other.

Consider a bird in flight. The wings move in perfect unity with each other to lift this dove into the air and take her where she wants to go. When we apply the Clean Living concept, it promotes a life that is in harmonic union, full of health, zest and joy.

It's All About Life

I am an average, everyday person just like you who found herself in extraordinary circumstances facing a serious choice. I could accept my medical situation as fate and treat continually worsening symptoms over the years, or I could become my own health advocate and change my future. You can figure out by now which one I chose.

I am still a work in progress and I diligently work on my health every day. I am not perfect and I don't have a "magic" pill that I can sell you for $29.95. I can only tell you what worked for me. To help you get started on your own plan for Clean Living, I have compiled a list of my personal favorites, from detox to smoothies, to the products I use to keep my house fresh and clean.

My Favorite Organic Smoothies

Smoothies are a delicious way to get the nutrients our bodies need. Try some of my favorite smoothies for yourself! Where you see kale, I use Curly, Lacinato, and Redbor interchangeably. If you are new to a fiber-rich diet, begin with a smaller amount of flax seed. Adjust the ingredient amounts accordingly to your taste and the manufacturer's recommendations for your blending device.

Once you've tried these recipes, don't be afraid to personalize your smoothies. I love to experiment with different combinations to create different tastes and boost my health benefits. I use a Vitamix for blending my smoothies.

Boost Me Up!

1 cup chopped kale

1/2 cucumber (small)

1/2 cup fresh raspberries

1/2 cup fresh blueberries

1 tangerine

1 banana

1/2 avocado

1 tbsp. golden flax seeds

1/2 cup water

1/2 cup almond milk

1. Combine all ingredients together in a blender. Blend on high until smooth.

2. If needed, consider adding more almond milk to achieve the preferred consistency.

Go Green!

2 cups chopped kale

1/2 cucumber

1/2 cup spinach

1/2 cup arugula

1/2 avocado

1 green apple

1 kiwi

1-2 sprig fresh mint

1/2 cup water

1/2 cup almond milk

1. Combine all ingredients together in a blender. Blend on high until smooth.

2. If needed, consider adding more almond milk to achieve the preferred consistency.

Feel Alive!

1 cup chopped kale

1 carrot, apple, pear, banana

1/2 avocado

1 tbsp. flax seeds

1/2 cup water

1/2 cup coconut milk

1. Combine all ingredients together in a blender. Blend on high until smooth.

2. If needed, consider adding more coconut milk to achieve the preferred consistency.

Wake Me Up!

1 cup chopped kale

1/2 cup arugula

1/4 cup pineapple

1/2 orange

1 sprig fresh spearmint

1/2 cup water

1/2 cup coconut milk

1. Combine all ingredients together in a blender. Blend on high until smooth.

2. If needed, consider adding more coconut milk to achieve the preferred consistency.

Rejuvenate Me!

2 cups chopped kale

1/2 cucumber

1/4 cup green grapes

1 cup honeydew melon

1/2 fresh lime

1/2 cup water

1. Combine all ingredients together in a blender. Blend on high until smooth.
2. If needed, consider adding more water to achieve the preferred consistency.

The Paper Cut Theory

What happens when you go off your food plan? Or when you fall off your schedule? That was one of my biggest concerns when I first started. *What will occur when I give into those tempting foods that have been calling my name?* Dr. Goldner had a great answer for me called the Paper Cut Theory.

Think of a time when you flipped through the pages of a book and got a paper cut. The sting is an ever-present, annoying distraction. But usually within 48 hours you don't even notice that it's there anymore.

When you are healthy and you go off your diet, it is similar to a paper cut, but as long you quickly go back to what you are supposed to be eating, it is not going to have an effect on your overall health. Don't beat yourself up about it; a break from your routine is not a disaster. Being able to recognize a break and returning to the Clean Living process is part of fresh thinking.

One habit I have found helpful is to buy healthier alternatives for some of my favorite snack foods. You know, the ones that seem impossible to resist? For me, it's potato chips.

There is something about them that makes them irresistible! The only way I manage to avoid eating them is by not having them in my home. I have found some snacks that kill that craving in a healthy way.

- Jackson's Honest Sea Salt Potato Chips made with Coconut Oil
- Siete Grain-Free Tortilla Chips made with Avocado Oil

My Eye Care Routine

Here is what I use to help my dry eyes. These products have made an enormous difference and I am so thankful for them.

- Carlson Norwegian Fish Oil Liquid
- Systane Eyelid Cleansing Wipes
- Systane Preservative-Free Eye Drops

I apply a warm compress to my eyes morning and night for 5-7 minutes and then follow with my Systane Wipes and apply my preservative-free eye drops.

Fish oil helps the body to retain moisture and restores balance to dry eyes. I add my fish oil to a glass of water every morning or I add it to my salad. It may take some time to acquire a taste for this, but the alternative is to use the soft gels.

My Exercise Routine

In addition to healthy, organic food choices, I maintain my body's flexibility and strength with thirty minutes of daily exercise. I prefer a combination of dance and yoga routines. I nurture my spirit and keep my mind in a clear, positive state by beginning my day with an opening prayer. In the evening, I end my day with meditation and a prayer.

My Home

The quality of the air we breathe is very important. Your lungs can absorb toxins through the air, which then goes on to the blood system to be transmitted throughout the entire body. These toxins can contribute to serious health consequences.

You may not be able to control what you breathe when you are out and about, but in your home, you are in full control. That is why I am very careful about the products I use to clean and detox my home. I am also concerned about our environment. Here are some of the ecologically-friendly products I use in my home:

- EcoKindness Cleaning Products
- doTERRA Essential Oils — I use these essential oils in my diffuser to freshen my air and to help alleviate symptoms
- GermGuardian Air Purifier

ৡ

What Comes Next?

There is a quote that challenges me every time that I hear it:

Life begins at the end
of your comfort zone.

Neale Donald Walsch

What is your comfort zone? One thing that I have learned is that your "comfort zone" is not always the comfortable place you imagine it to be. It may feel "good" but it isn't good for your overall health. Clean Living is a natural, healthy lifestyle, but it requires active, intentional choices to make the process successful.

Traditional medicine often takes a piecemeal approach, emphasizing medication to address individual symptoms, rather than a holistic perspective that addresses both the person and their environment as an interwoven web. Of course, the complexity of such a health care model demands more engagement from the individual person to meet their health goals.

Most doctors are caring professionals dedicated to making people well and saving lives. They work hard and many spend long hours studying the latest research so that their knowledge stays current. But a typical family doctor will see anywhere from 18 to 30 patients on an ordinary day – with an average patient base of over 2,100 people, there isn't enough time to cover the factors that come from the body, mind and environment during a typical office visit.

My diagnosis was a powerful wake-up call. I *knew* that there had to be more for me to learn so that I could experience healthy living again. It was a terrible feeling to discover that staying in my "comfort zone" led me to a very uncomfortable place.

That is why I am encouraging you to become your own health detective and advocate. Take the time to explore Clean Living and live like never before!

Clean Living begins by building your knowledge. It is time to claim your Fit and Nourished Body, your Forward-Thinking Mind, and turn your home into a Fresh, Free Environment. Let's review the key points of each of the three aspects of Clean Living.

A Fit and Nourished Body

Maintain the amazing body you have been given to experience the world by living a healthy, fit and nourished life. Let's review the four critical areas that affect your body's health: detoxifying, alkalinity, exercise and rest.

Detox Your Body

Detoxifying is an excellent way of clearing your body of toxins and pollutants. It gives your organs a thorough cleaning so that they can function at their highest level to heal your body.

Alkalinity

When the pH in your body is low, it creates an acidic environment where your body cells start to break down, resulting in conditions where disease and sickness can flourish. By eliminating acidic foods from our diet and eating raw, organic foods and drinking alkalized water, it will bring your body to an alkaline state.

Exercise

Exercise is a wonderful way to keep your body in excellent shape. Stay interested by finding ways that are fun for you. Many people find that exercising with a friend helps them be accountable. Here are some ideas to try:

- Bicycling
- Dancing
- Walking
- Hula Hooping
- Kick Boxing
- Martial Arts
- Rock Climbing
- Rollerblading
- Swimming, including just laps or aquafit classes
- Team Sports such as soccer, hockey, baseball
- Zumba

Rest

Don't neglect your need for sleep. Your body is designed to rejuvenate during periods of rest. Restrict your caffeine and screen time to encourage restfulness. A full night's sleep (7-9 hours) will help you to be more productive during the day.

Your Forward-Thinking Mind

Keep your mind decluttered, so you are not in a state of constant overwhelm. Every month or so, repeat the thought-tracking exercise from Chapter Four and monitor your progress. Practice speaking aloud from a "greatest hits" list of affirming thoughts.

Your goal is to have healthy, peaceful, positive thought patterns that allow you to make the right choices in life based on what is best for you, so that you can accomplish your goals and dreams. If you are struggling, please seek support.

And finally…

Your Fresh, Free Environment

Take the time to craft a nurturing, uncluttered

home space. Some homes need organization to a degree where it is tempting to ignore the problem rather than deal with the clutter.

Don't rationalize or procrastinate with "I'll get around to it some day" — this is taking its toll on your body and mind.

Put a plan in place to declutter your home and take regular action to maintain it. You will be amazed at how little time it takes to keep your house clean and fresh once you have purged what you don't need. Your home will become the clean, inviting and rejuvenating sanctuary you deserve.

Your Time Is Now!

It is my hope and prayer that this book has been of help to you and encourages you to take the next steps on your journey to Clean Living. This book comes from my heart. My desire is to guide you to a better life where you have a fit, nourished body; a forward-thinking mind; and a fresh, free environment that brings you peace and restores your body, mind and spirit.

If you need more help, I have two tools to help you. On the next page, I have a list of resources that I use on a regular basis. They will be a good starting point in your own research as a health detective.

The best way for me to help you is to connect with you personally. I love working one-on-one and with groups to help people take the next steps. So, if you want personal coaching, media productions or to have me as a keynote speaker at your next event, go to www.patriciadiesel.com/contact. Fill in the form and I will contact you.

As I close, I want to leave you with this quote:

The secret of health for both
mind and body is not to mourn
for the past, not to worry about
the future, or not to anticipate
troubles, but to live the present
moment wisely and earnestly.

Siddartha Guatama Buddha

Helpful Resources

Helpful Books For Your Body, Mind & Environment

Body:

CLEAN Remove, Restore, Rejuvenate
Author: Alejandro Junger, M.D.

Energetic Health; Interesting Insights Into Advanced Natural Medicine
Author: Dr. Henele

Guide To Medicinal Herbs
Author: National Geographic

Goodbye Lupus
Author: Brooke Goldner, M.D.

Spontaneous Healing
Author: Andrew Weil, M.D.

Mind:

Awaken The Giant Within
Author: Tony Robbins

Conversations With God
Author: Neale Donald Walsch

Life Coaching; A Guide to Hiring a Professional Coach
Author: Patricia Diesel

The Code of the Extraordinary Mind
Author: Vishen Lakhiani

The Power of Now
Author: Eckhart Tolle

The Power of Positive Thinking
Author: Dr. Norman Vincent Peale

Environment:

A Simple Guide to an Organized Life
Author: Patricia Diesel

Blissful Organization
Author: Patricia Diesel

Buried in Treasures
Author: David F. Tolin, Gail Steketee, David O. Frost

Conquering Chronic Disorganization
Author: Judith Kolberg

Life Recovery for the Cluttered Soul
Author: Patricia Diesel

About The Author

PATRICIA DIESEL — a leading clutter expert, lifestyle coach and national speaker is the founder of Keep It Simple Now, a professional organizing and life coaching company that offers individual and corporate services.

Patricia is an accomplished columnist and author of Uncluttered, A Guide to Hiring a Professional Coach, Emily's Mannequin; A Year of Awakening, Life Recovery for the Cluttered Soul, Blissful Organization and A Simple Guide to an Organized Life.

She has been featured in publications such as Woman's Day, Cosmopolitan, New England Hoarding Consortium and her media appearances include The Learning Channel, Good Morning America, Lifetime Networks, The Morning Show and Healthology.

Patricia is a Certified Professional Life Coach from The Institute of Professional Coaching (IPEC), a National Speaker and member of the National Speaker Association

(NSA), a Chronic Disorganization Specialist holding Certificates of Study in Chronic Disorganization from the Institute for Challenging Disorganization (ICD), and past member of the National Association of Professional Organizers (NAPO).

Patricia understands the journey to healing — and the power of clean living. She has dedicated her life to helping people restore tranquility and a sense of order to their lives through her transformational lessons.

INVITE PATRICIA TO SPEAK AT YOUR EVENT

To invite the author to speak to your group or organization, you can contact her at:

Email: Patricia@patriciadiesel.com

Phone: (908) 642-1226

Website: www.patriciadiesel.com

Clean Living

Notes

www.patriciadiesel.com

Clean Living

Notes

Clean Living

Notes

Clean Living

Notes

Clean Living

Notes